Saint George
and the Dragon

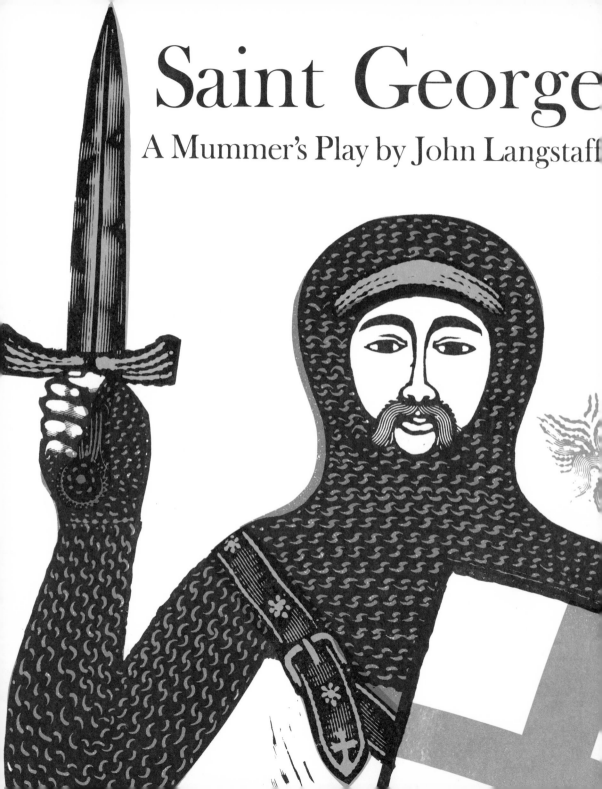

Saint George

A Mummer's Play by John Langstaff

and the Dragon

with woodcuts by David Gentleman

A Margaret K. McElderry Book

Atheneum   1973   New York

Library of Congress catalog card number: 73-75437
ISBN: 0-689-30421-8
Published simultaneously in Canada by McClelland & Stewart, Ltd.
Manufactured in the United States of America
Printed by Connecticut Printers, Inc., Hartford, Connecticut
Bound by A. Horowitz & Son/Bookbinders, Clifton, New Jersey
First Edition

Saint George and the Dragon

Folk plays like this are known to exist all over the world, and, wherever they appear, they always contain some symbolic contest, as well as a "medicine man," or clown figure, who restores the fallen hero to life and ensures the victory. The champion, killed and then revived, symbolizes the triumph of life over death, light over darkness, spring over winter. The audience usually participated in some way at the conclusion of a performance by sharing food, giving contributions or, as in our version, singing or dancing together. This was a ceremonial way of bringing good luck to everyone, just as the Old Year turned and the New Year was about to begin.

Even though the original purpose of primitive ritual is obscured today, three vestiges of it remain. First, the folk plays are still performed only at certain important seasonal times of the year; second, the form of presentation is usually in a ceremonial manner, with the players standing in a semicircle; and, finally, the actors disguise themselves in some simple way, not to be recognized by their friends in the audience. (Anonymity insures the good luck.) Often these actors were known as *mummers* and traveled about with their play to farmyards, houses, kitchens or halls like the *wassailers* or *waits* who sang carols through the streets at Christmas. In some of the oldest examples of the folk play, the traditional sword dance is a particularly important part of the action. With makeshift swords, often agricultural or fishermen's implements, the intricate weaving patterns of the dance culminate in a woven "star" of swords—a perfect hexagon or the ancient pentagonal design.

No matter how amateurish the actors, this play, the present version of which is compiled from several variants, always "catches" its audience, so long as the actors project the play's boisterous broad humor and fun mixed with the solemn moments of mysterious magic in the sword dance and ritual revival.

"Please to let the mummers act!"

John Langstaff

Saint George
and the Dragon

ROOM
scampers in,
clears the stage
and announces the play

Room, room, brave gallants all!
Pray give us room to rhyme.
We've come to show activity
Upon this wintertime.
Activity of youth, activity of age,
Such activity as you've never seen
on stage!

ROOM

Though some of us be lit - tle, and some of a mid - dle sort;
We all de - sire your fa - vor to see our plea - sant sport. __

FATHER CHRISTMAS
enters majestically

Here comes I, Old Father Christmas.
Welcome or welcome not,
I hope Old Father Christmas
Will never be forgot.
Christmas comes but once a year,
But when it comes it brings good cheer:
Roast beef, plum pudding, strong ale and mince pie . . .
Who likes that better than I?

Although they call me Old Father Christmas,
I have but a short time to stay.
I've come to bring you pleasure and pastime
Before I go away.

Walk in, Johnny Jack, I say
And boldly clear the way.

JOHNNY JACK *sidles in, with several dolls tied on his back*	In comes I, happy Johnny Jack, With my wife and family on my back. My family is large and I am small— I've brought my broom to sweep your hall.

Roast beef, plum pudding, strong ale and mince pie . . .
Who likes that better than Old Father Christmas and I?

FATHER CHRISTMAS   Nobody!

JOHNNY JACK Step in, Fool,
And show the people sport and play
Before tonight we go away.

The clown or "magic man" enters with Old Bet,
the "man-woman," on his arm.

FOOL

Ye gen-tle-men all who in mirth take de-light and in-
Al-though I am lit-tle, my strength it is great. I would

tend__ our sport for to see;__ I've come for to tell you that I am the clown. And
scorn for to tell you a lie.__ I once kill'd a hedge hog as big as my-self, and it

pray you how do you like me?__ And pray you how do you like me?__
made me a rare ap-ple-pie!__ And it made me a rare ap-ple-pie!__

My father killed a great fat hog,
And this you may plainly see;
For this is the old bladder
Out of his hurdy-gurdy-gee!

Fool turns to tease Old Bet.

FOOL
Ma - dame I have come to court you, if your fav - or I should win.
If you make me kind - ly wel - come, then per - haps I'll come a - gain.

**OLD BET
AND FOOL**
*dancing
together*
Fol the rol the rid - dle all the ray - do, fal the ral the rid - dle all the ray,
fol the rol the rid - dle all the ray - do. Fal lal lal the rid - dle all the day.

**FOOL
OLD BET**
Ma - dame I have rings and jew - els, Ma - dame, I have house and land.
What care I for your world of jew - els, what care I for your house and land.

Ma - dame I've the world of trea - sure, if you'll be at my com - mand.
What care I for your world of trea - sure, all I want is a hand - some man!

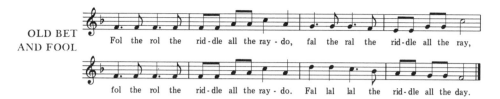

OLD BET
AND FOOL   Fol the rol the rid-dle all the ray-do, fal the ral the rid-dle all the ray,

fol the rol the rid-dle all the ray-do. Fal lal lal the rid-dle all the day.

GIANT   In comes Giant Blunderbore, fee, fi, fum!
thunders in,   Ready to fight you all, so I says come!
brandishing his club

If I could meet St. George here,
I'd put my spear in through his ear.
I'd cut him, I'd slash him as small as flies,
And send him to Jamaica to make into mince pies!

OLD BET AND FOOL   "Mince pies hot,
hand clapping   Mince pies cold;
Send him to Jamaica e'er he's nine days old!"

Giant rushes at them.
They dodge aside, and the Fool calls out:

FOOL   Come in, come in, thou Hobby Horse!

HOBBY HORSE
gallops in gaily,
waving his hat in the air

Over mire and over moss,
In comes I, the Hobby hoss!

Make room, make room, my boys and gals,
Pray give me room to ride.
I've come to show activity this merry Christmastide.
A Dragon you shall see—
A "Wild Worm" for to flee!

Come in, come in, thou dragon stout,
And take thy compass round about.

DRAGON
"Speckleback" roars in,
stomping around the stage
and frightening everyone

Stand on head, stand on feet,
I want meat, for to eat!

I am the Dragon, here are my jaws!
I am the Dragon, here are my claws!

Meat, meat, meat, for to eat!
Stand on head, stand on feet!

The Dragon fights the Giant and knocks him over.

FOOL
speaking mysteriously
to the audience

St. George shall come and die by swords
Which circle round his neck.
As Winter dies, so shall he die,
And rise as Spring again!

ST. GEORGE *comes forth heroically*

Here come I, St. George, from Britain did I spring.
I'll fight the Dragon bold, my wonders to begin.
I'll clip his wing, he shall not fly,
I'll cut him down, or else I die.

DRAGON

Who's he that seeks the Dragon's blood
And calls so angry and so loud?
With my long teeth and scurvy jaws,
I'll tear the flesh from off his nose!

ST. GEORGE

Stand off, stand off, thou Dragon bold,
Or by my sword thou'lt die.
I'll pierce thy body full of holes,
And make thy buttons fly!

They circle about one another, clawing and thrusting.

DRAGON

My body's made of iron,
My head is made of steel,
My claws are made of beaten brass;
No man can make me feel.

ST. GEORGE

No one could ever frighten me,
For many I have slain.
I long to fight, 'tis my delight
To battle o'er again.

They fight, and the Dragon is knocked down.

FATHER CHRISTMAS
hails St. George
triumphantly

Step forth, St. George, thou champion!

ST. GEORGE
moves forward and
solemnly addresses the
audience

First comes Christmas,
Then comes Spring.
Like Winter I must die,
Then to life again like Spring!

Shouts to Sword Dance team to enter:

Dance, men, the Sword Dance now for me.

*Six dancers file in to music and perform figures
of the sword dance— (see directions page 47) —
Toward the end of the dance, St. George goes into the
center, and the sword lock is made around his neck. He
falls over, the willing victim, when the swords are drawn.*

CAPTAIN
(*Sword Dance Team*)

See what we have done.
We have cut him down like the evening sun!

Let two take his feet and two take his arm,
And we'll carry him out like a ship in a storm.

*As team starts forward to move St. George, Father
Christmas stops them.*

FATHER CHRISTMAS

Horrible! Terrible! What have you done?
You have killed my dearly beloved son!

Oh, oh, is there a doctor to be found
To cure this deep and deadly wound?

ACTORS
*shouting ad lib
to the audience*

Doctor! A doctor! Please, a doctor! Doctor!

FATHER CHRISTMAS

A doctor, a doctor!
Is there a doctor to be found
Can quickly raise my noble son
Lies bleeding on the ground?

JOHNNY JACK
*pointing to
the approaching doctor*

See, sir, a doctor here!

DOCTOR
*riding in on horse-
back, accompanied by
his servant, Finney*

Here I am, John Brown,
The best quack doctor in this town!

I am the doctor from Spain,
To fetch the dead to life again.

FATHER CHRISTMAS   How cam'st thou to be a doctor?

DOCTOR   By my travels.

FATHER CHRISTMAS   Where have you traveled?

DOCTOR   Italy, Spittaly, France and Spain,
Germany, Iceland, and back again.
I've seen houses thatched with pancakes high; roads
paved with dumplings; plum pudding growing in berry
trees, and little pigs running about with knives and
forks in their backs crying, "Who'll eat me? Who'll eat me?"

FATHER CHRISTMAS   Can you cure my son?

DOCTOR
*passes out a few marsh-
mallows and throws
some out to the audience*   Take these here my pills. They cure the young, the old,
the hot, the cold, the living, and the dead!

Doctor stumbles over corpse.

What the devil's the matter here?

FOOL   A man's dead seven minutes. Can you cure him?

DOCTOR   If he's dead seven years I can cure him!
Hold my hoss, Jack Finney.

JACK FINNEY   My name ain't Jack Finney, my name's Mr. John
Finney, a man of great strength.

FINNEY   Will he bite?

DOCTOR   No.

FINNEY   Will he kick?

DOCTOR   No.

FINNEY   Take two to hold him?

DOCTOR   No.

FINNEY   Hold him yourself then!

DOCTOR   What's that? You saucy young rascal!
swats at Finney

FINNEY   Oh, I hold him, sir. I've got fast hold of his tail!

DOCTOR   Bring me my spyglass, Mr. John Finney.

FINNEY   Fetch it yourself, sir.

DOCTOR   What's that, you saucy young rascal?

FINNEY   Oh, I fetch it, sir. There it is, sir.

DOCTOR   What's throw it down there for?

FINNEY   Ah, for me to pick to up again, sir.

DOCTOR   What's that? You saucy young rascal!
cuffs Finney again

FINNEY   Ah, for me to pick it up again, sir.

FATHER CHRISTMAS   Pray, doctor, what sort of diseases can you cure?

DOCTOR   The All Sorts.

FATHER CHRISTMAS   What's the All Sorts?

DOCTOR   All sorts of diseases, whatever you pleases.
I am the doctor that can cure all ills.
Only gull up my potions and swallow my pills.
I can cure the itch, the stitch, the palsy and gout,
All pains within and pains without.

Here's a box of my pills. Take one tonight, and two in the morning, and swallow the box at dinnertime. If the box don't cure you, the lid will!

FATHER CHRISTMAS   You must be a clever doctor.
You'd better try your skill.

DOCTOR
goes to St. George and lifts his feet   Thank you, sir, and that I will.
Come, old fellow, raise up your head.

FINNEY   That ain't his head.

DOCTOR   What is it then?

FINNEY   His stommicks!

Doctor drops his feet

DOCTOR	Let him take a drop of my Inkum-pinkum mixed up with cat's feathers. Have a drop in his eye, a drop in his nose, and a drop in his mouth.

Any better, old fellow?

OLD BET   You silly man, the dead man never stirs.

DOCTOR   Oh Bet, I quite forget. I have taken the right cork off the wrong bottle!

I have a little bottle in my inside-outside pocket which I call the "Okum-pokum." A little drop on his forehead, a little drop on his heart; rise up again, and take they part!

OLD BET   That's not cured the man.

DOCTOR   Take a drop of another bottle that'll go down you thrittle-throttle. Rise up and fight for old England again! Open they flip-flop, and take this "slip-slop." . . .

FATHER CHRISTMAS   Well, doctor, he's a long time coming back to life.

FOOL   Stand aside; I'll fetch him back to life.

pushes the Doctor aside and takes over with great solemnity

If this man's not dead, but in a trance,
We'll raise him up and have a dance!

The Fool makes magic signs over St. George, while the cast watches spellbound. He straightens the legs and arms, lays the sword on St. George's chest, and, taking a sprig of holly from the Hobby Horse nearby, he places it on the body.

St. George slowly arises, as out of a deep sleep.

ST. GEORGE

Good morn - ing, gen - tle - men,____ a - sleep - ing I have been.____
But now I am a - wake,____ a - live un - to this day.____

I've had such a sleep as the like was nev - er seen.____
Our danc - ers shall have a dance and the doc - tor take his pay.____

| DRAGON | We all shake hands, never fight no more; |
| | All be brothers as we ever was before. |

| GIANT | We wish you a Merry Christmas and a joyful New Year, |
| *addressing audience* | And Spring come soon to fill us all with cheer! |

| HOBBY HORSE | A pocket full of money and a cellar full of beer |
| *prancing forward* | And a good fat pig in the pigsty to last you all the year! |

FATHER CHRISTMAS	Be there loaf in your locker and sheep in your fold,
	A fire on the hearth and good luck for your lot,
	Money in your pocket and a pudding in the pot!

*Cast turns to audience and sings the Mummers' carol,
inviting everyone to join in.*

God— bless the mas-ter— of this house, the— mis-te-ress al

so, And all the lit-tle chil-dren— that round the ta-ble

go,————— that round——— the— ta-ble go.

ROOM   Our Play is done; we must be gone,
We stay no longer here.
We wish you all, both great and small,
A happy, bright New Year.

EXEUNT

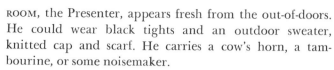

ROOM, the Presenter, appears fresh from the out-of-doors. He could wear black tights and an outdoor sweater, knitted cap and scarf. He carries a cow's horn, a tambourine, or some noisemaker.

In some English villages the entire troop of mummers was traditionally dressed or disguised in paper costumes: newspaper or colored paper cut in long streamers, attached all over the clothing and hanging from a tall paper hat. This would make a fine, weird costume for Room.

FATHER CHRISTMAS is a fairly recent addition to this ancient play. This patriarchal bearded figure, dressed in a long colorful robe and cap, carries a lantern and a staff decorated with the symbolic holly and ivy.

JOHNNY JACK is a spry, agile character who traditionally "sweeps" the playing area to be used—a most important aspect to the success of the play! He can be dressed in either ragged clothing or a belted tunic, with an old straw hat or a hat with a feather. He carries his "family" on his back: either dolls pinned to his back or a string of dolls tied together over his shoulder. A long-handled hearth broom would be appropriate.

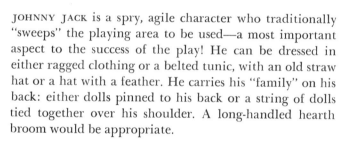

THE FOOL is the most important character in the folk play. He is full of fun, but also clever and magical. Even our circus clowns today still have some of these inherited attributes. He is not a "court jester" type. At the end of the play he actually turns out to be the powerful witch doctor. The base of his costume can be a pair of ordinary white pajamas, with many small animal figures and symbols, cut out of colored materials sewn, on all over. He wears a tall, conical hat with ribbons and carries a blown-up bladder tied to the end of a short stick—a balloon will do.

OLD BET is another ritual character, the "man-woman," found in many of the folk cultures of the world, including the American Indian's today. It's a masquerade for one of the men or boys, costumed in an old-fashioned

dress. A parasol, a pocketbook, a shawl about the shoulders, and even a sunbonnet, add to the slapstick part. It is best to choose the deepest voice available, or a boy's voice in the process of changing, as Old Bet must definitely sound like a man imitating a woman.

THE GIANT will probably be the tallest actor and should be as fierce looking as possible. His costume might include baggy, dark trousers with big patches sewn on, very high fishing boots, a wide belt or sash, enormous workman's gloves, and a turban or big, black felt hat. He carries an enormous club (a stick padded and wrapped with layers of dark cloth), and he could have false features and thick, bushy eyebrows.

THE HOBBY HORSE is a symbolic life-giving figure familiar to many parts of the world, including the Pueblo Indians of North America. A wide hoop must be made out of light strips of wood or heavy wires to encircle the waist of the actor. A papier-mâché or a wooden horse's head is fastened to the front of the hoop. This is all attached to the actor by straps that loop over his shoulders and is held steady by the reins he grasps from the horse's head. A colorful skirt hangs from the frame, so that we only see his feet as he prances about with bells attached to his ankles. The "rider" wears a shoulder cape, bedecked with ribbons, and a plumed hat, which he can wave as he rides.

THE DRAGON should be so scary that he makes the youngest spectators shriek when he comes lurching toward the audience! The creation of this frightening creature can be done with papier-mâché for the head (large enough to fit over the actor's head and open enough to hear his voice clearly), and a green speckled body made from an old piece of curtain with scales painted or sewn on. Claws for the hands can be made from stiff paper, and skin-diving flippers can add a webbed effect to the feet.

ST. GEORGE probably came into the Mummer's play considerably later than its primitive beginnings. His splendid costume can be simply managed with gray tights, over which a very loosely knit shirt, sprayed with silver paint, will give the illusion of chain mail. He carries a sword and a shield emblazoned with his red cross.

THE DOCTOR is the blustering, "ordinary man" on the outside of these magical characters of power and deeds. He wears an old frock coat or a tailcoat, a bowler or top hat, white gloves, spectacles, and a fake moustache. He carries an old carpetbag or suitcase, which contains an enormous bottle marked "poison," and an assortment of gruesome looking carpenter's tools, such as a hacksaw, large pliers, brace and bit, a length of thin rubber hose, outdoor weather thermometer for taking temperatures, and a bag of marshmallows (which he can toss as pills to the audience).

JOHN FINNEY is a traditional "fall guy" and takes all the slapstick beratings and pratfalls. Finney can be dressed nattily in sporty gear: riding breeches and boots, waistcoat and walking stick or crop.

THE DOCTOR'S HORSE can add a great deal of hilarious fun to the play. Two boys hidden under a large blanket, holding a constructed horse's head out in front, make a good animal. Finney leads the horse in with the Doctor astride. The horse kicks up his heels at various characters on stage. His tail consists of a long length of very thick rope, which can be let out or taken in by the rear boy. (Finney never lets go the tail, which must be able to stretch out and contract as Finney gallivants around the stage.)

THE SWORD DANCERS are of utmost importance to the mystery and magic of the play. They are dressed alike in white shirts and either light or dark trousers. They can wear colorful bandannas wrapped around their heads, sashes around their waists, and bright bands of ribbon crisscrossing their chests. Each man carries a wooden sword, which is a slat of wood about a yard long, smoothed out at the hilt end for grasping.

THE SWORD DANCE
(very abbreviated)

With swords carried over their right shoulders, six dancers enter single file, winding about to form a circle moving clockwise. A rhythmic springy tread or short running step is used continually throughout the dance. Tunes like "The Girl I Left Behind Me" or "God Rest Ye Merry Gentlemen" could be used at a fast tempo.

Still moving clockwise, the dancers rhythmically clash their swords in the center high above their heads (16 times). Then the swords are lowered to the side and, making a larger circle, each man grasps the point of his neighbor's sword. This linked circle never stops moving. Two dancers move across the circle together (shoulder-to-shoulder), the sword between them held at chest height, to pass under the arch formed by the opposite pair of dancers in the circle. The dancers on either side follow them. After they lead under, they turn away from each other (turning under their swords) and go back to their places, passing their swords over the heads of the dancers following them. At the same time, the two dancers making the arch accommodate the dancers passing beneath their swords by moving a little forward. Then they turn together under their swords as the circle again opens out. This "double-under" figure is repeated, with other couples in the circle moving across to an arch formed by two other dancers each time.

The team continues to circle left but closes in. Never releasing the hilt of his own sword, which is in his right hand, each man simultaneously, crossing his left hand *under* his right, passes the point in his left hand to his neighbor on the right and receives, in his own right hand, *along with his hilt,* the point of his left-hand neighbor's sword. He then frees his left hand and with it takes hold of the point passed to him. All cross their right wrists *under* their left (hilts under points) and the "lock" is formed. Swords are tightly, securely, and quickly meshed together in the form of a double triangle or a woven six-pointed star, and the leader grasps one of the hilts and raises the entire "lock" above his head as the dancers continue to move. St. George walks into the middle of the moving ring and stands in the center. The "lock" is lowered over his head. Each man grasps the hilt of his sword, steadying it as the circle continues about the victim, so that the swords do not touch his neck or shoulders. At a given signal, the dancers all draw their swords and St. George falls.

THE SUSSEX MUMMERS' CAROL

Piano arrangement by Marshall Barron

God__ bless the mas - ter__ of this house, the__ mis - te - ress al - so, And all the lit - tle chil - dren__ that round the ta - ble go,_____ that round_____ the__ ta - ble go.